Secrets of
the World's Greatest
Sex
Doctors

Bottom Line
Books
www.BottomLinePublications.com

CONTENTS

First printing

Bottom Line Books® publishes the advice of expert authorities in
many fields. These opinions may at times conflict as there are often different
approaches to solving problems. The use of this material is no substitute for
health, legal, accounting or other professional services. Consult competent
professionals for answers to your specific questions.

Telephone numbers, addresses, prices, offers and Web sites listed in this book are
accurate at the time of publication, but they are subject to frequent change.

Bottom Line Books® is a registered trademark of Boardroom® Inc.
281 Tresser Boulevard, Stamford, CT 06901

www.bottomlinepublications.com

Bottom Line Books® is an imprint of Boardroom® Inc., publisher of
print periodicals, e-letters and books. We are dedicated to bringing
you the best information from the most knowledgeable sources in the
world. Our goal is to help you gain greater wealth, better health,
more wisdom, extra time and increased happiness.

Printed in the United States of America

TWH/am

SEX
SECRETS

DR. JOY BROWNE TALKS ABOUT SEX

Source: Psychologist **Joy Browne, PhD.** One of her books is *It's a Jungle Out There, Jane* (Three Rivers Press).

During my nationally syndicated daily radio show on WOR Radio Network, people ask all kinds of questions about sex.

WHAT THEY ASK MOST OFTEN...

What can I do when my partner says I'm too tired?

The first time it happens, don't take it personally. Just listen, and offer solace and maybe a back rub. But if a pattern emerges, it's time to go on a fact-finding mission. Tiredness can stem from overwork or depression. Or it can be a way of saying *I'm angry with you.*

NOTE: Don't raise the subject in the bedroom, where your partner is likely to feel defensive.

WHAT TO SAY: You seem to be tired a lot lately. Are you having problems at work? Are you angry with me? Or is something else making you tired?

Once you track down the cause, you can start to work on the *real* problem.

I fantasize about being with someone else when I make love with my partner. Is this normal?

There is nothing wrong with fantasizing. Everyone does it. And fantasy can be useful because it helps us discover the discrepancy between what we have and what we want.

EXAMPLE: If you often fantasize about someone who is more aggressive in bed than your partner, it is probably time to talk about either your spouse's or your passivity.

If you fantasize about a situation—a place where you have sex, for instance—you might want to share this with your partner. It could increase your mutual enjoyment. But if you fantasize about another person, don't tell your partner. It will only cause pain.

HOW MUCH IS TOO MUCH: If your sex life is 10% fantasy, that's okay. But if it's 90% fantasy, it's not healthy.

REASON: Part of the joy of lovemaking comes from the intimacy you establish with your partner. If you constantly distance yourself by fantasizing, you miss out on the benefits of that relationship.

My spouse flirts a lot. What can I do about it?

First, examine your marriage.

ASK YOURSELF: Is this a symptom of a larger problem? If it is, you and your partner should seek counseling.

If, however, you are generally happy with your relationship, look at the context of the flirting. Does it always happen at parties? In public? A certain amount of flirtation is natural in social situations—as long as it's not carried beyond that level.

Flirting in a happy marriage can become a problem if it is used in a manipulative way, to say, *Look—other people find me attractive!* This is an early sign of instability.

NOTE: If you're unhappy with yourself—if you've gained a few pounds, for instance—you may be especially sensitive to your partner's flirting. It may seem worse than it really is.

I found out that my partner is having an affair. What should I do?

Most affairs are a symptom of a greater problem in the marriage.

ASK YOURSELF: Do I want to stay with this person? Am I willing to let it go on indefinitely? Am I willing to leave?

If you try to ignore the affair, say nothing and hope that it will burn itself out naturally, you will become angry and your trust in your spouse will be destroyed.

BETTER: Tell your partner that you understand that these things happen, but that you can't live with him/her under the circumstances. He must move out until he decides what he wants. Don't guarantee that you'll be there if he decides to come back.

He may decide to break off the affair and try to save the marriage. But if he leaves, you must decide if you want to wait, or separate.

We don't have as much sex as we once did. Is this unusual?

Most couples experience great passion when they first become physically involved. They spend weekends in bed and delight in making love in strange and wonderful places.

But a sexual relationship, like anything else, loses some of its novelty over time. And many things—a new job, a baby, etc.—can affect the libido and disrupt a sexual pattern.

At the beginning of a relationship, some people try to adapt their behavior to fit the other person's sexual tastes. As the relationship continues, however, they gradually begin to reassert their own wishes. And old patterns may no longer be acceptable.

EXAMPLE: Early in the relationship, Andy took the initiative sexually. But once they had been married for a few months, he grew tired of always being the instigator and relaxed his efforts. Carolyn began to think he wasn't interested in her anymore.

If the change is not comfortable for either partner, the couple should talk about why things have changed and what measures each can take to alter the pattern.

Changes could involve being more seductive, going away for weekends, balancing sex in the morning (which many men prefer) with sex in the evening or even remembering the power of an occasional quickie.

What can we do to make our sex life more interesting?

Figure out what things can be changed, what you've both outgrown, what has become a stale habit.

KEY INGREDIENT FOR GOOD SEX: Making each other feel appreciated.

We remember our first sexual experiences as being quite wonderful—when they probably weren't—because someone made an effort to make us feel needed and special.

Good sex has very little to do with positions. It has to do with what's in our head, and that's easy to change.

EXAMPLES: Put some adventure into your sex life—show up in a trench coat and nothing else, slip a sexy note into your partner's pocket or purse, wear fun clothes...send a *different* kind of flowers than usual...go back to the restaurant where you had your first date.

Your surprises should show your partner your special knowledge of his likes and dislikes. A hot fudge sundae by candlelight will speak volumes to a spouse with a sweet tooth.

■

MACA: THE SUPER FOOD THAT HELPS WITH YOUR SEX DRIVE

Source: **Mark A. Stengler, NMD,** licensed naturopathic medical doctor in private practice, Stengler Center for Integrative Medicine, Encinitas, California...adjunct associate clinical professor at the National College of Natural Medicine, Portland, Oregon...author of many books, including *The Natural Physician's Healing Therapies* and coauthor of *Prescription for Natural Cures* (both from Bottom Line Books).

Super foods are foods and herbs considered to be especially healthful due to their hefty nutritional content. The list includes familiar favorites, such as blueberries, broccoli and beans. Now a more exotic super food you may never have heard of is generating excitement in the world of natural health—a Peruvian root vegetable called maca (*Lepidium meyenii* or *peruvianum*), pronounced MACK-ah.

The root of the maca is shaped like a large radish. It is a cousin to other cruciferous plants, such as cauliflower and brussels sprouts. Peruvians traditionally boil or roast the maca root or grind it into flour for baking. However, despite maca's popular description as a "super food," you won't see it in food form in this country. Instead, the root is dried and ground into a fine powder. It then is distributed primarily in capsules, although you also can buy the powder to blend into beverages or sprinkle on foods.

I began looking into maca for my patients about seven years ago. In addition to its healthful fiber, complex carbohydrates and protein, maca provides numerous minerals, including calcium, magnesium, phosphorous, potassium, sulfur, iron, zinc, iodine and copper...vitamins B-1, B-2, C and E...nearly 20 amino acids, including linoleic acid, palmitic acid and oleic acid...as well as various plant sterols, which are natural cholesterol-lowering agents. All of these nutrients have been shown to promote health in a multitude of ways.

Here is what this super food can do for you...

BOOST SEX DRIVE...

Legend holds that in the era of the Inca empire, battle leaders provided maca to warriors to enhance their strength—then cut off the supply after the fighting ended to protect women from the warriors' maca-heightened libidos.

Modern research has suggested that maca does indeed increase sex drive in men. One double-blind, randomized study published in the journal *Andrologia* examined the effect of maca on sexual desire in 57 men, ages 21 to 56. Participants took either placebos or 1,500 mg or 3,000 mg of maca daily. After four, eight and 12 weeks, they reported on their sex drive levels. Placebo users experienced no change in libido, while the men taking either quantity of maca reported heightened sexual desire starting at eight weeks and continuing throughout the study.

HOW IT WORKS: Maca's libido-enhancing powers are attributed primarily to its amino acids and sterols, among other properties. Blood tests indicated that maca did not affect the men's levels of the hormones testosterone or estradiol (a form of estrogen present in women and men). This is just one of maca's virtues—it does not change hormone regulation in men.

A small study published in the *Asian Journal of Andrology* yielded some interesting results, indicating that maca also improves male fertility. Nine men, ages 24 to 44, received either 1,500 mg or 3,000 mg of maca per day. Compared with tests done at the outset of the study, semen analysis performed at the end of the four-month research period demonstrated that maca increased semen volume, sperm count and sperm motility at both dosage levels. Again, maca achieved these results by unknown mechanisms that were not related to increases in testosterone or other hormones.

HOW TO GET YOUR MACA...

I recommend organically grown maca products from Natural Health International, or NHI (888-668-3661, *www.naturalhi.com*, available online or through naturopathic doctors). The company sells a blend for women called Femmenessence MacaPause® (the same blend used in the study of Polish women, who experienced significant improvement in their menopausal symptoms) and another for men, Revolution Macalibrium, formulated to enhance energy and vitality in men as they age.

DOSE: The average dosage of maca supplements is 1,000 mg to 2,000 mg daily, which you can take anytime.

You can also sprinkle maca powder into your favorite foods and drinks. The powder is available online from *www.navitas naturals.com*, *www.superorganicfoods.com* and *www.iherb.com*. Maca has a slightly nutty flavor and so I recommend mixing it with almond milk.

Other ideas...

• *Sprinkle on cereal* (hot or cold)
• *Mix into your favorite smoothie or protein shake*
• *Add to yogurt or applesauce,* perhaps with a little cinnamon
• *Stir into tea*—especially chai blends, as the flavors complement each other
• *Use in baking*—substitute maca powder for ¼ of the flour in any recipe (any more and it may affect texture or consistency).

BE AWARE: Maca has a high fiber content and may initially cause gas. Gradually I suggest beginning with 1 teaspoon a day, then gradually increasing your intake by one teaspoon every five days, until your find your comfort zone. The optimum dosage is three to six teaspoons per day.

■

ASK FOR WHAT YOU WANT IN BED

Source: **Judy Kuriansky, PhD,** clinical psychologist and sex therapist on the adjunct faculty of Columbia University Teachers College in New York City. She is author of many books, including *The Complete Idiot's Guide to a Healthy Relationship* (Alpha). *www.drjudy.com*.

Sexual satisfaction eludes many women—but you don't have to settle for so-so sex.

SOLUTION: Tell your partner what pleases you. HERE'S HOW...

• *Figure out what turns you on.* If you are not sure what feels good, spend private time pleasuring yourself...when you and your partner have sex, pay attention to what excites you.

FOR INSPIRATION: Read *Pleasure* by Hilda Hutcherson, MD (Perigee).

• *Recognize that your partner isn't a mind reader.* Many women think, "If he loved me, he'd know how to please me"—but most men need to be taught. To avoid hurt feelings, explain, "As my body has changed, so have my desires. Let's experiment to see what feels best now."

• *Don't say don't—say do.* If I say, "Don't think of a pink elephant," what's the first thing you think of? A pink elephant. Only afterward does the brain compute the "don't." The same thing happens when you tell your partner, "Don't squeeze my breasts"—which may lead him to inadvertently repeat the unwanted behavior.

BETTER: "It excites me when you kiss my breasts."

• *Show and tell.* Put your hand over his, and show him how to stimulate you. Describe in detail what you want—"Please run your fingers slowly up my thigh"—then respond with enthusiasm.

■

IS THE G-SPOT A MYTH?

Source: **Judy Kuriansky, PhD,** clinical psychologist and sex therapist on the adjunct faculty of Columbia University Teachers College in New York City. She is author of many books, including *The Complete Idiot's Guide to a Healthy Relationship* (Alpha). *www.drjudy.com.*

The G-spot is not a myth—it is a highly erotic area that can enhance a woman's sexual pleasure at any age. It is located on the front wall of the vaginal "barrel," about one-third of the way up. Compared with the smoothness of the rest of the vaginal wall, the G-spot (more accurately called an "area") feels slightly rippled. When a woman is aroused, blood rushes to the area. G-area stimulation may trigger an emission of fluid that helps moisten the vaginal opening—a plus for older women, for whom dryness can be a problem.

Positions that work best to stimulate the G-area during intercourse include the woman on her back with a pillow under her bottom and the man on his knees before her...doggie position, with the man angling his thrusts downward...and the woman on top, guiding the man's thrusts to contact the G-area.

■

EASTERN PRACTICES FOR BETTER SEX

Source: **Lori Brotto, PhD,** assistant professor of obstetrics and gynecology, and director, Sexual Health Laboratory, University of British Columbia, Vancouver, Canada, and leader of an article published in *The Journal of Sexual Medicine.*

Women with low libido who began a regular practice of mindfulness (a meditative focus on the moment) reported improved sexual arousal. Women with a genital pain disorder who received a varying number of acupuncture treatments in areas linked to the liver, spleen and kidneys reported reductions in pain. Both groups reported increased vaginal lubrication and sexual satisfaction.

■

YOU'RE NEVER TOO OLD TO CATCH AN STD

Source: **Kimberly Workowski, MD,** associate professor of medicine at Emory University and chief of the guidelines unit in the epidemiology and surveillance branch of the Division of STD Prevention at the Centers for Disease Control and Prevention, both in Atlanta. *www.cdc.gov/std.*

Painful urination or vaginal discharge may make you suspect a bladder or yeast infection—but those symptoms could instead signal a sexually transmitted disease (STD). Though people tend to associate STDs with adolescents and young adults, doctors report an alarming rise among older patients. REASONS...

• *Erectile dysfunction drugs allow older men to be more sexually active than before.* The more partners you have—and the more partners your partner has had—the greater your STD risk.

• *Condoms reduce the risk for catching some STDs*—but after menopause, when there is no need for contraception, couples are far less likely to use condoms.

• *As women age,* the vaginal wall thins and lubrication diminishes, leaving tissues more prone to damage and infection during sex.

PLAYING IT SAFE...

The surest ways to avoid getting an STD are to abstain from sex, including oral sex, or to be in a long-term relationship in which you both are monogamous. OTHERWISE...

• *Before beginning a new relationship,* you and your potential partner should both get tested for STDs.

• *Have your male partner use latex condoms consistently.*

• *If you develop STD symptoms,* stop having sex and see your doctor promptly.

• *If an STD is diagnosed,* abstain from sex (including oral sex) until treatment is completed.

• *Your current partner must be tested and treated at the same time* so he doesn't reinfect you.

• *Notify anyone else with whom you had sex in the last six months* —he should get checked, too.

WHAT TO WATCH FOR...

Some STDs can be cured with antibiotics. For other types there is no cure—so contagion control is essential. BE ON THE LOOKOUT FOR...

• *Chlamydia.* This bacterial infection of the genital tract is so widespread that testing is recommended for all sexually active women age 25 or under...and for women of any age who have a new sex partner or multiple partners.

SYMPTOMS: Some women experience pain when urinating and/or an abnormal vaginal discharge...many others have no early symptoms. If infection spreads to the fallopian tubes, it can cause serious pelvic inflammation, intense pain and infertility. Men may have a penile discharge or pain when urinating.

MEDICAL CARE: Diagnosis is based on a urine test or a cervical swab. Treatment is one dose of the antibiotic *azithromycin* (Zithromax) or a seven-day course of *doxycycline*.

• *Genital herpes.* This viral disease stays in the body indefinitely, causing repeated outbreaks.

SYMPTOMS: Women and men develop painful genital ulcers (blisters) that can take several weeks to heal...women may have difficulty emptying the bladder.

MEDICAL CARE: Diagnosis is made with a viral culture. There is no cure, but outbreaks diminish in frequency and severity over time. An oral antiviral drug, such as *famciclovir* (Famvir) or *valacyclovir* (Valtrex), taken daily or at the start of an outbreak, minimizes symptoms.

CONTAGION CONTROL: To reduce the risk of catching or passing on herpes, always have your male partner use a latex condom—the virus can be transmitted even in the absence of active symptoms. Abstain from sex (oral sex, too) during outbreaks.

• *HIV (human immunodeficiency virus).* Everyone who is evaluated for an STD and all pregnant women should be screened for HIV infection. Some people with HIV infection develop acquired immunodeficiency syndrome (AIDS).

SYMPTOMS: Signs may develop within weeks or may not appear for up to 10 years. Early symptoms are vague—fever, malaise, skin rash. Later symptoms include severe diarrhea, weight loss, chills, and vulnerability to other infections and some cancers.

MEDICAL CARE: Blood or saliva tests are used for diagnosis. With the Home Access HIV-1 Test System (about $44 at drugstores), blood is collected from a finger prick and mailed in for testing. Individualized drug combinations can significantly slow disease progression.

CONTAGION CONTROL: To minimize the risk of contracting or transmitting HIV, correct and consistent condom use is recommended.

• *HPV (human papillomavirus).* Certain HPV strains cause genital warts in women and men. HPV can lead to cervical cancer and other malignancies in women. HPV also is linked to some oral cancers in people infected through oral sex.

SYMPTOMS: Warts appear as small flesh-colored growths—flat, raised or cauliflower-shaped—on or around the genitals. They may itch and may bleed with intercourse.

MEDICAL CARE: Genital warts are diagnosed visually. Tests for HPV infection can be done along with a Pap test...or if Pap results are abnormal. Warts can be removed with topical medication, laser or other methods—but may recur.

CONTAGION CONTROL: Usually HPV goes away on its own.

BEST: Get regular Pap tests (following the schedule recommended by your doctor), which can detect early cellular changes from HPV infection.

• *Trichomoniasis.* A protozoan parasite causes this. Women may develop vaginal symptoms from a recent sexual encounter ...or from one that occurred years or even decades ago due to lingering infection in the glands surrounding the urethra.

SYMPTOMS: Women develop frothy, smelly, greenish vaginal discharge...genital itching...and/or discomfort during intercourse and urination. Men may have a slight penile discharge or a burning sensation upon urination or ejaculation.

MEDICAL CARE: Women are diagnosed with a lab test of vaginal secretions...men get a urine culture or urethral swab. Usually a single dose of the antibiotic *metronidazole* (Flagyl) or *tinidazole* (Tindamax) cures the infection.

YOGA MAY IMPROVE SEX FOR WOMEN

Source: **Lori Brotto, PhD,** assistant professor of obstetrics and gynecology, and director, Sexual Health Laboratory, University of British Columbia, Vancouver, Canada, and leader of an article published in *The Journal of Sexual Medicine.*

Some women have trouble focusing when making love. In yoga, you are encouraged to concentrate on how the body responds to each pose. This can make it easier to tune in to sexual sensations as well. Most types of yoga can provide this benefit.

EXERCISE BOOSTS SEX LIFE

Source: **Lonnie Barbach, PhD,** assistant clinical professor of medical psychology, University of California Medical School, San Francisco, and author of *Turn Ons* (Plume).

Couples who exercise together report better relationships on many levels, including sex.

REASONS: People who work out feel better about their bodies …working out releases brain chemicals that make women and men feel energetic and happy…and working out together makes them feel better about being with each other.

TALKING ABOUT SEX MAKES IT BETTER

Source: **E. Sandra Byers, PhD,** professor of psychology, University of New Brunswick, Fredericton, Canada, whose study was published in *Journal of Sex Research.*

Men and women who tell their partners about their sexual likes and dislikes report better sexual relationships—and higher overall relationship satisfaction.

AVOIDING SEX MAKES SEX WORSE

Source: **Barry McCarthy, PhD,** department of psychology, American University, Washington, DC, writing in *Journal of Sex & Marital Therapy*, 325 Chestnut St., Philadelphia 19106.

A common myth says that being nonsexual for a time increases desire. This is not always true. Regular sexual contact creates positive anticipation and pleasure in sex. Avoidance leads to anxiety and tension.

HELPFUL: If two weeks go by without sexual contact, the spouse with higher desire initiates a sexual date within a week. If he/she does not do this, the other spouse takes responsibility for initiating a sexual date the next week.

■

YOU DON'T HAVE TO SETTLE FOR A SEXLESS MARRIAGE—WHY COUPLES STOP MAKING LOVE...AND HOW TO REIGNITE THE PASSION

Source: **Joel D. Block, PhD,** assistant clinical professor in the department of psychiatry and behavioral sciences at Albert Einstein College of Medicine in New York City, and a senior psychologist at North Shore-Long Island Jewish Medical Center in New Hyde Park, New York. A couples' counselor and sex therapist in private practice in Plainview, New York, Dr. Block is the author of numerous books, including *Sex Over 50* (Perigee). *www.drblock.com.*

A lot of longtime couples still share love and respect...but the sexual sizzle has fizzled to the point where they hardly ever make love.

This has two potentially grievous consequences.

FIRST: In many cases, only one partner is content with the status quo—so the other person's frustration eventually threatens the relationship.

SECOND: Physiologically, sex becomes a "use it or lose it" proposition as we age—so with prolonged abstinence, permanent problems with arousal, erection and/or orgasm often develop.

Does this situation sound familiar? Unless you are prepared to risk your marriage or give up on sex forever, you need to take action. **HERE ARE REASONS WHY SEX GOES INTO LIMBO—AND WAYS TO BRING IT BACK...**

• *Health issues.* **SEE YOUR PHYSICIAN—AND HAVE YOUR HUSBAND SEE HIS—TO DISCUSS THE FOLLOWING...**

• An undiagnosed medical problem could be causing your sexual shutdown. *Example:* Diabetes can reduce blood flow and cause nerve damage, leading to frustrating erectile dysfunction (ED) or extreme vaginal dryness. Treating the underlying problem often restores a satisfying sex life.

• Medication can interfere with sex. Cholesterol-lowering statin drugs can reduce *testosterone*, a hormone that influences sex drive...certain antidepressants suppress libido by decreasing levels of *dopamine*, one of the brain chemicals that fuel desire...some blood pressure drugs can limit blood flow to the genitals, hindering arousal and orgasm. Switching medication often solves the problem.

• Psychological stumbling blocks can arise from physical ailments—such as when a person recovering from a heart attack feels too anxious to risk the exertion that sex involves. *Helpful:* Ask your doctor for guidelines on safe activities.

• Aging often leads to ED—so ask your partner to talk to his doctor about medications that help produce erections. If direct penetration still isn't possible, encourage him to bring you to orgasm manually, orally or with a vibrator...and express your love with caresses and kisses.

• ***Poor body image.*** You may be embarrassed about your wrinkles or weight—or turned off by his. BEST...

• Let go of idealized images of the past. Think realistically about your early sexual encounters—the awkwardness of being inexperienced in bed, the fears of unwanted pregnancy, the pain when a relationship ends. To appreciate your body today, reflect on how much more skilled you now are as a lover...the joy of being free from pregnancy concerns...and the security of a hug from someone who has loved you for years.

• Focus on physical pleasures—even when not in bed. Take scented baths together. Give each other leisurely massages. Build up your partner's sex appeal, in his mind and in yours, with a gift of silk boxers.

• Make the first move yourself if you feel frustrated as you wait for your partner to initiate sex. Your boldness will be a turn-on. If you're never in the mood when he reaches for you, ask to be seduced—with roses, poetry, candlelight.

• ***Lack of communication.*** Some couples make contentious topics taboo—political views, a daughter's divorce—to avoid conflict. But as bans increase, communication and intimacy stall. HELPFUL...

• Make your bedroom a "trust zone"—where you both promise to talk openly without arguments, criticisms or stony silences. When the bedroom is a sanctuary from emotional storms, it feels more natural to put down your defenses, share confidences...and make love.

• Remind your partner that sexual needs change over time. For most older men, the mere thought of sex is no longer enough to produce an erection—so ask him what kind of direct manual or oral stimulation arouses him. Postmenopausal women often need a lubricant, so buy one—such as Astroglide or longer-lasting K-Y Silk-E Vaginal Moisturizer—and tell him (or show him) erotic ways to stroke it onto your genitals and his.

• *Hidden anger.* Many couples believe that they're "too tired" for sex, but the real chill comes from suppressed anger. **TO TRY...**

• Consider possible sources of resentment. Maybe your husband loses desire because your bedroom closet reminds him of how you chronically overspend on clothing. Perhaps you turn away when you recall his long-ago and supposedly long-forgiven fling. *Clues:* Subtle digs ("Sure, your new black dress is as pretty as the old one—is it a bigger size?")...or withdrawal ("Nothing's wrong, stop asking").

• Focus on bothersome behavior rather than attacking your partner's character. *Example:* Say, "I feel insecure when you flirt with the neighbors," not, "You act like the neighborhood stud."

• See a therapist if you have trouble curbing behaviors that fuel justifiable anger or making peace with the past. *Referrals:* American Board of Professional Psychology, 919-537-8031, *www.abpp.org.*

• *Boredom.* Being able to predict what your partner will do, in and out of bed, makes sex ho-hum. **THE FIX...**

• Learn new sexual techniques by watching sensual films together. *Check out:* Femme Productions from Candida Royalle, 800-456-5683, *www.candidaroyalle.com.*

• Experiment with sex toys. Even if they are only good for a giggle, it's great to laugh together in bed. *Discreet source:* Good Vibrations, 800-289-8423, *www.goodvibes.com.*

• Pretend it's your third date. Dress up...go someplace new ...avoid too-familiar topics (job, house, kids)...share old secrets and new insights. You'll be amazed—and aroused—to discover the wonderful ways in which the man you thought you knew so well has evolved.

MORE HELP: If the steps above do not revive your sex life, consult a sex therapist.

REFERRALS: American Psychological Association, 800-964-2000, *http://locator.apa.org.*

SEX HELPS YOU FEEL BETTER

Source: **Alexander Mauskop, MD,** director, New York Headache Center, New York.

Sex boosts the immune system—and can help prevent colds and headaches. People who averaged one to two sexual encounters per week had higher levels of *immunoglobulin A*—which protects against disease. And people who had sex two or three times a week reported fewer migraine headaches—because sex releases hormones that prevent migraines.

FANTASIES MAKE SEX BETTER

Source: **Eric Klinger, PhD,** professor of psychology, University of Minnesota at Morris.

People with the most active sex lives have the most sexual daydreams.

FOR BETTER FANTASIZING: Realize sexual daydreaming does not mean you are dissatisfied with sex itself or with your partner. You can daydream anywhere—whenever the mood strikes, whether you are alone or with your partner. If you have trouble thinking of sexual fantasies and wish to do so, sexy books or movies are a good way to trigger them.

LESS SEX

Source: **Domeena Renshaw, MD,** founder/director, Loyola University sexual dysfunction clinic, Maywood, Illinois.

Married couples today have sex less frequently than couples 60 years ago. Then, married men and women in their 30s had sex about three times a week. Now the average is about twice a week.

POSSIBLE REASONS: Dual-career marriages and other elements of a high-pressure modern lifestyle.

CURES FOR BEDROOM BOREDOM

Source: **Pepper Schwartz, PhD,** renowned expert on sexuality. She is professor of sociology at University of Washington, Seattle...board member of the Sexuality Information Council of the United States...and past president of the Society for the Scientific Study of Sexuality. She is author of a dozen books, including *Everything You Know About Love and Sex Is Wrong* (Putnam) and *Ten Talks Parents Must Have with Their Children About Sex and Character* (Hyperion).

For most couples, the frequency and intensity of lovemaking decline dramatically over time.

On average, newlyweds have sex at least three times a week. Lovemaking drops to twice a week after the first year... once a week after 10 years...and two or three times a month after 20 years. About 10% of couples have no sex at all after 20 years of marriage.

Sexual relationships lose their zing when couples get in the habit of making love the same way...in the same place...at the usual time. **HERE ARE 10 CURES FOR SEXUAL BOREDOM...**

GET AWAY FROM HOME...

Couples often tell me that they only have good sex—or any sex—during vacations. This is the only time when they feel relaxed...away from the distractions of home...and totally focused on each other.

Of course, you needn't wait for a full-fledged vacation. Go away for the weekend—or check into a hotel for a night.

Abstain from sex for at least a week before your getaway. Going without makes you want it even more.

DON'T WAIT UNTIL NIGHT...

Couples usually wait until night to make love—but fatigue is the enemy of good sex. Set aside an hour or two during the day.

If you've got kids at home, send them to a friend's house or Grandma's. You may have sex less often, but the sex you do have will be more intense.

SET THE SCENE...

Turn off overhead lights, especially harsh fluorescents. Light candles. Or use peach or blue bulbs, as *Playboy* photographers do, to create a seductive glow. Spray a touch of perfume in the air. Or put out a bouquet of lilacs. Scent subtly changes the environment, making you feel that you're in a different place, which is exciting.

Couples seldom bother with music after they are married. That's a mistake.

Try *Bolero* if you like classical...Sade for sensual singing... Frank Sinatra's love songs...Bonnie Raitt's *Let's Give Them Something to Talk About*. For younger ears—listen to the music of Train or Sting.

WEAR SOMETHING SEXY...

It's a great way to turn on your partner—and to feel sexy yourself. A man might wear silk boxers or tight briefs.

Some women are reluctant to wear lacy lingerie if they feel overweight. Not a size 6? So what. Wear something free-flowing and transparent. Your partner will love it.

WATCH EROTIC DVDs...

Watching other people make love can be a turn-on.

BEST DVDs FOR COUPLES: *Alexandra...Andrew Blake's House of Dreams...Burgundy Blues...Candida Royalle's Christine's Secret...Hidden Obsessions.*

TAMER FILMS WITH STEAMY SEX SCENES: *An Officer and a Gentlemen...Bull Durham...From Here to Eternity...The Big Easy.*

TRY DIFFERENT POSITIONS...

There's nothing wrong with the traditional missionary position, but why limit yourself? There are scores of other positions to try. *The New Joy of Sex* illustrates hundreds of different maneuvers.

OTHER GOOD SOURCES: *Anne Hooper's Ultimate Sex Guide* and *The Art of Tantric Sex.*

HELP THINGS ALONG...

A woman's natural lubrication diminishes as she gets older. Every couple should get in the habit of using lubricants. Apply it before things heat up.

GOOD CHOICES: K-Y Silk-e and K-Y Liquid, sold at most drugstores. Another good lubricant is Albolene—but *not* if you use condoms. It contains petroleum, which quickly breaks down latex.

TRY A SEX TOY...

A vibrator is usually used to stimulate the woman. Some men find it pleasurable used gently on the penis. It can also stimulate the outer anal area, which is loaded with pleasurable nerve endings. Lubricate the area first.

Best vibrators...

• *Pocket Rocket.* If you are new to vibrators, this is a good one to start with. It is small, about three inches long. You can use it alone at first, then with your partner as you become more comfortable.

• *Hitachi's Magic Wand*—many women like it because it is more powerful than other wands and has a variety of attachments.

• *The Rabbit* stimulates the vagina and the clitoris.

WEAR A BLINDFOLD...

This allows you to focus more on the tactile sensations. It intensifies your anticipation because you don't know where or when you will be touched.

Wearing a blindfold also makes you feel slightly submissive, which can be erotic. Take turns wearing the blindfold.

EXPLORE YOUR FANTASIES...

Everyone has sexual fantasies—though many people are too embarrassed to act on them.

That's unfortunate because creative playacting can lead to intense erotic encounters. Consider talking about fantasies with your partner—then make them happen.

■

MARRIED PEOPLE VS. SINGLE PEOPLE

Source: **Linda Waite,** professor of sociology, University of Chicago, and coauthor of *The Case for Marriage* (Doubleday).

Married people have sex more often than single people do—*and enjoy it more.* About 40% of married people say they have sex at least twice a week, compared with about 20% of single people who are not living with a partner.

REASONS: Sex fits more easily into married life than into singles' lives...married people have more incentive to please their partners and more time to learn how to please them ...married sex creates a satisfying emotional bond.

■

SURPRISING SCENTS CAN MAKE YOU MORE SEXUALLY APPEALING

Source: **Alan Hirsch, MD,** neurological director, Smell & Taste Research and Treatment Foundation, Chicago, and author of *Scentsational Sex* (Element).

There are many scents available at any given time, but there are some scents that are associated with arousal. **HERE ARE SOME SCENTS THAT WOMEN AND MEN RESPOND TO SEXUALLY...**

WOMEN: Arousal is strongest with combinations of Good 'n Plenty candy plus cucumber or banana-nut bread.

TURNOFFS FOR WOMEN: Men's cologne...cherries...barbecued meat.

MEN: Every tested scent increased male arousal.

COMBINATIONS THAT ELICIT THE STRONGEST MALE RESPONSE: Lavender and pumpkin...doughnuts and black licorice... pumpkin pie and doughnuts.

■

SECRETS OF GREAT SEX

Source: **Dagmar O'Connor, PhD,** sex therapist in private practice, New York City, and author of the book and video packet *How to Make Love to the Same Person for the Rest of Your Life—and Still Love It* (Dagmedia, *www.dagmaroconnor.com*).

Here are six ways that will increase sexual pleasure and intimacy with your partner...

• *Communicate and clear up resentment.*

• *Share honestly what you want from sex.*

• *Do not fight or discuss problems in bed*—it should be a place for rest and pleasure.

• *Once a week, touch each other for an hour* without focusing on orgasm.

• *Share sexual fantasies* if you and your partner are ready for this intimacy.

• *Touch each other often when not in bed* to create a sense of closeness all the time.

■

SEX IS A GOOD PAINKILLER

Source: **Ronald Lawrence, MD, PhD,** founding member, International Association for the Study of Pain, Seattle, and coauthor of *Preventing Arthritis* (Putnam).

Orgasm releases morphine-like compounds called *endorphins*, which relieve pain and promote relaxation. Many arthritis patients report relief for one to two hours after orgasm. That is as long as a morphine injection lasts.

■

BETTER SEXUAL SATISFACTION

Source: **Rodney Francis, MD,** obstetrician-gynecologist in private practice, Santa Monica, California.

To increase vaginal lubrication, drink at least eight glasses of noncaffeinated, nonalcoholic beverages every day. When the body does not get enough fluids, it pulls moisture from other areas, including vaginal membranes. This makes sex uncomfortable.

■

BETTER SEX AFTER SERIOUS ILLNESS

Source: **Leslie R. Schover, PhD,** professor of behavioral science, University of Texas M.D. Anderson Cancer Center, Houston.

Plan lovemaking for a time when you are rested and relaxed. Don't look at sex as a performance. Expect some difficulties at first, and discuss your concerns ahead of time. See a doctor if intercourse is difficult for physical reasons, such as vaginal pain and dryness or inability to get firm erections.

■

COMMUNICATION IS KEY

Source: **Eva Margolies,** director, Center for Sexual Recovery, New York. She is author of *Undressing the American Male: Men with Sexual Problems and What You Can Do to Help Them* (Plume).

Schedule talks about sex until you and your partner become comfortable talking without preplanning. After intimacy, try telling each other something that pleases you and something you would like to change.

MYTH: Most people are satisfied with whatever their partners do during sex.

REALITY: Sexual likes and dislikes differ greatly because of physical and emotional variations among men and women. It is almost impossible to have a good sex life without openly discussing your preferences.

SEX MAKES YOU LOOK YOUNGER

Source: **David J. Weeks, PhD,** clinical neuropsychologist, Royal Edinburgh Hospital, Scotland, and leader of a 10-year study of 3,500 people ages 18 to 102, published in *Sexual and Relationship Therapy.*

People who have loving sex at least three times a week look more than 10 years younger than the average adult.

POSSIBLE REASONS: Sex is pleasurable and produces feel-good chemicals...and loving couples keep themselves in shape for each other.

HOW TO GIVE A SENSUAL MASSAGE

Source: **Victoria Day,** massage therapist and registered midwife, Bristol, England. She is author of *A Lover's Guide to Massage* (Ward Lock, distributed by Sterling Publishing Co.).

Start a sensual massage by putting oil on your hands and applying it to your partner with broad, easy strokes. Be very gentle at first, then feel through your fingers where to press harder. Keep your fingers relaxed. Use your whole palm and fingers for the massage. Keep strokes reliable and rhythmic, so the massage feels like a continuous sequence even though you move from one body part to another.

■

PAY CLOSE ATTENTION WHEN GIVING A SENSUAL MASSAGE

Source: **Victoria Day,** massage therapist and registered midwife, Bristol, England. She is author of *A Lover's Guide to Massage* (Ward Lock, distributed by Sterling Publishing Co.).

S ensual massage encourages couples to create a time and place to be alone together, focused only on each other.

WHEN GIVING A MASSAGE: Ask your partner if there are parts of his/her body in need of special attention. Focus entirely on your partner, concentrating on using your hands. Be open to whatever your partner wants.

■

INTIMATE SECRETS

Source: **Susan Crain Bakos,** author of several books on relationships and intimacy, Jersey City, New Jersey including *Sexational Secrets: Exotic Advice Your Mother Never Gave You* (St. Martin's Press).

K iss the inside of your partner's wrist to feel his/her pulse and warm your lips. Brush your lips lightly against his…take his face in your hands…put your lips on his…and press gently while looking into his eyes. Kiss lightly and playfully for several minutes before closing your eyes and kissing with passion.

■

BETTER SEX

Source: **Jack Morin, PhD,** psychotherapist and sex therapist in the San Francisco area. He is author of *The Erotic Mind: Unlocking the Inner Sources of Sexual Passion and Fulfillment* (HarperPerennial).

G ive your partner regular, positive feedback about what feels especially good. This builds his/her confidence and increases the chances that you'll receive more of what you enjoy. Wait until you're feeling close to discuss sexual problems and dissatisfaction rather than when either of you is defensive, tired or preoccupied. Talk about times you were together that were particularly pleasing so you can learn what turns each other on.

DIFFERENT LEVELS OF DESIRE

Source: **Joel D. Block, PhD,** assistant clinical professor in the department of psychiatry and behavioral sciences at Albert Einstein College of Medicine in New York City, and a senior psychologist at North Shore-Long Island Jewish Medical Center in New Hyde Park, New York. A couples' counselor and sex therapist in private practice in Plainview, New York, Dr. Block is the author of numerous books, including *Sex Over 50* (Perigee). *www.drblock.com.*

B eing sexually out of sync happens now and then to most couples and does not signal disaster.

IF YOUR PARTNER IS RELUCTANT: Find other ways of being close...and be particularly attentive to your partner's needs when he/she desires intimacy. Don't take it personally—the lack of interest may reflect fatigue, stress or something else that has nothing to do with you.

TIMING IS EVERYTHING

Source: **Al Cooper, PhD,** clinical director, San Jose Marital and Sexuality Centre, San Jose, California.

A fulfilling sexual experience can take just minutes or hours —and the time that one experience lasts does not predict how long the next one will take. Research reports that cite average times are misleading. Even a person's own average time has little relevance.

REASON: There is no normal time before climax during intercourse. And sexual preference varies from day to day...and person to person.

■

BETTER SEX STARTS IN THE BRAIN

Source: **Joel D. Block, PhD,** assistant clinical professor in the department of psychiatry and behavioral sciences at Albert Einstein College of Medicine in New York City, and a senior psychologist at North Shore-Long Island Jewish Medical Center in New Hyde Park, New York. A couples' counselor and sex therapist in private practice in Plainview, New York, Dr. Block is the author of numerous books, including *Sex Over 50* (Perigee). *www.drblock.com.*

To improve lovemaking, think about it during the day...and call your loved one to share your thoughts and get him/her thinking about it, too.

• *Be romantic.* The right setting—lighting, temperature, aroma, attire, flowers, etc.—sets the mood.

• *Progress slowly.* Don't rush to finish. Savor all of the sensations you experience.

■

EASY ROUTE TO A BETTER SEX LIFE

Source: **Joel D. Block, PhD,** assistant clinical professor in the department of psychiatry and behavioral sciences at Albert Einstein College of Medicine in New York City, and a senior psychologist at North Shore-Long Island Jewish Medical Center in New Hyde Park, New York. A couples' counselor and sex therapist in private practice in Plainview, New York, Dr. Block is the author of numerous books, including *Sex Over 50* (Perigee). *www.drblock.com.*

Allow yourself small pleasures regularly—such as a hot bath or a movie matinee—so you and your partner can relax and enjoy sexuality. Schedule at least one hour a week just for you and your spouse. Do not watch TV at night—play a board game, read out loud or do something else to bring yourselves closer. Do not discuss anger-provoking issues near bedtime. If you're always too tired to make love, try setting the alarm for 90 minutes after you fall asleep or for one hour earlier in the morning and make love then. And don't worry about frequency. *Quality matters more than quantity.*

■

HOW SEX THERAPY WORKS

Source: **Marc Agronin, MD,** assistant professor of psychiatry, University of Minnesota Medical School, Minneapolis. He is author of *A Woman's Guide to Overcoming Sexual Fear & Pain* (New Harbinger Publications).

The therapist is a mental-health professional trained to treat people with sexual problems. Usually you meet him/her weekly to discuss assignments in sexual behavior that you carry out at home. Various sexual practices and positions, erotic materials and sexual aids may be recommended, depending on your personal situation. Sex therapists do not physically examine patients or have any physical contact with them.

■

SEXUAL MYTHS

Source: **Marc Agronin, MD,** assistant professor of psychiatry, University of Minnesota Medical School, Minneapolis. He is author of *A Woman's Guide to Overcoming Sexual Fear & Pain* (New Harbinger Publications).

Sex is wonderful if you love your partner. In reality, good sex is learned. Love can be a strong foundation, but good sex also requires learning what pleases your partner and increases his/her desire and passion.

MYTH: Male and female sexuality are the same.

REALITY: Men and women experience sex differently. Women's responses vary widely. Partners need to identify their own sexual feelings and discuss them.

MYTH: Good sex is spontaneous.

REALITY: Sex planned into busy lives can be just as enjoyable as spontaneous sex.

■

PORNOGRAPHY *DOES* TURN ON WOMEN, JUST AS IT STIMULATES MEN

Source: Study by researchers at the Ludwig Boltzmann Institute for Urban Ethology, Vienna, Austria, of the response of 10 men and 10 women to a 15-minute sex film, reported in *New Scientist,* Kings Reach Tower, Stamford St., London, England SE1 9LLS.

B oth males and females show significant increases in the sex hormone testosterone after watching a pornographic film. Men's testosterone tends to increase more, but the increase in women is also substantial. The more testosterone a woman produces during her monthly cycle, the more sexually active she tends to be.

▦

TO KEEP YOURSELF KISSABLE

Source: **Lou Paget,** sexuality educator, Los Angeles, and author of *How to Be a Great Lover* (Broadway Books).

W e have collected three ways to keep yourself kissable. **THEY ARE EASY TO DO...**
  • *Carry breath mints*—and keep a small box by the side of the bed to beat morning breath.
  • *If you or your partner eat spicy or strong foods,* the other person should eat some.
  • *If his/her breath isn't fresh, take a mint for yourself*—and then offer one to him.

■

KISS YOUR SPOUSE FOR 10 SECONDS...

Source: **Felice Dunas, PhD,** acupuncturist and sexuality expert, West Hills, California, and author of *Passion Play: Ancient Secrets for a Lifetime of Health and Happiness Through Sensational Sex* (Riverhead Books).

A n intense 10-second kiss is rare in the midst of busy schedules. For that reason, it rekindles romance—tapping into the love beneath the trivia of everyday life. Give your spouse a warm, full-body hug, too. Both of you will feel good—and it is good for children to see their parents in a loving embrace.

■

THE 20-SECOND KISS CAN REVIVE THE FEELINGS THAT BROUGHT YOU TOGETHER

Source: **David LeClaire,** founder, Keeping Love Alive program, Seattle. He is author of *Bridges to a Passionate Partnership* (Equestrian Press).

A long, slow, deliberate kiss—which need not progress to further sexual activity—can be a great reviver of closeness. Simply agree that either of you can ask directly for a 20-second kiss when feeling underloved or underappreciated.

ALSO HELPFUL: The 60-second hug. Use it to say good-bye or to reconnect after a busy day. About halfway through a long hug, you will relax in each other's arms and feel a great release of tension.

■

VIBRATOR USE LINKED TO SEXUAL HEALTH

Source: **Debra Herbenick, PhD, MPH,** research scientist, department of applied health science, Indiana University, Bloomington, and leader of a survey of 2,056 women ages 18 to 60.

More than 52% of US women surveyed had used a vibrator ...24.3% had done so within the previous month. Compared with nonusers, vibrator users reported more sexual desire, arousal, lubrication and orgasms...had less pain...and were more likely to have had a recent gynecologic checkup.

■

RELATIONSHIP SECRETS

WEATHER THE FINANCIAL STORM TOGETHER

Source: **Judy Kuriansky, PhD,** clinical psychologist and sex therapist on the adjunct faculty of Columbia University Teachers College in New York City. She is author of many books, including *The Complete Idiot's Guide to a Healthy Relationship* (Alpha). *www.drjudy.com.*

An economic downturn doesn't have to damage your marriage.

BETTER: TO BE A TEAM WHEN MONEY IS TIGHT...

• *Banish money worries from the bedroom.* Many men (and some women, too) are vulnerable to letting their financial portfolios affect their libido and/or performance in bed. Assure your partner that he/she is sexy regardless of his/her bank account ...remind yourself that you are desirable and compassionate.

• *Reaffirm your values.* On a scale of one to 10, what do you rate higher—love or luxuries? Focus on caring, not cash, when you feel frustrated about the cost of fixing the dent your husband put in your car.

- *Learn together.* Make a date to attend free lectures on money management and stock market strategies (check your local library). Read aloud to each other from magazines on personal finance.
- *Propose a friendly competition.* See who can clip the most coupons or find the best deal on a lawn mower—promising the winner a back rub.
- *Have more fun—for less.* You may need to scale down your dreams, but you don't have to give them up. Your own hometown can be as romantic as Paris when the two of you stroll around admiring the architecture or enjoying picnics in the park.

WHAT IS THE DIVORCE RATE?

Source: **Betsey Stevenson, PhD,** assistant professor of business and public policy, The Wharton School of the University of Pennsylvania, Philadelphia.

The divorce rate is dropping. Among college-educated men who married in the 1970s, about 18% divorced within 10 years. That figure fell to 15% for men married in the 1980s and 13% for those married in the 1990s.

POSSIBLE REASON: Many couples are delaying marriage—and people who marry after age 25 are less likely to divorce than those who marry earlier.

PUT THE SIZZLE BACK IN YOUR MARRIAGE

Source: **Pepper Schwartz, PhD,** professor of sociology at University of Washington, Seattle, and senior fellow of Council on Contemporary Families. She is author of several books, including *Everything You Know About Love and Sex Is Wrong: Twenty-Five Relationship Myths Redefined to Achieve Happiness and Fulfillment in Your Intimate Life* (Perigee).

Stresses on marriage are everywhere today, and opportunities to cheat abound.

Dual careers and harried schedules already mean that many married people live separate lives. Add a stressful or lost job, retirement or an empty nest, and a disconnected spouse easily can question the marriage itself and his/her spouse's commitment. Lack of intimate involvement in a spouse's life can destroy a marriage even if neither partner strays—but you *can* keep your marriage strong.

HOW TO STAY CONNECTED...

It is normal for even happily married people to be sexually attracted to others and to fantasize about them. If attraction to other people makes you uneasy—or if you worry about your commitment to marriage or your ability to resist temptation —discuss the subject with a professional therapist.

It is relatively easy to reinvigorate your relationship with your spouse. **WHAT TO DO...**

• *Weave your lives together.* Look for activities that you both can enjoy. Find ways to support each other. Even when your spouse is out of town, keep in touch and find ways to be helpful.

EXAMPLES: Forward his essential e-mails...continue working on a task that you are doing together...do some advance work on a big home project that he is planning to do when he returns.

• Take the marriage off autopilot. Break your routine and have some fun. Take a trip together to somewhere you've never been...join a wine-tasting club...take dancing lessons. Try any pastime that brings you together.

• Secretly plan a weekend away, a night on the town or a candlelight dinner at home. You might be surprised at the joy you get from pleasing your spouse, not to mention the pleased response.

• Stir your spouse's emotions. Do some of the things that you both enjoyed when you first met—see movies...share books...play board games after dinner.

Or pick activities that will move you together emotionally. Pleasure from spectator sports, theater and concerts continues long after the event is over.

• Get physical. For many couples, sexual desire declines after years of marriage. Refresh that closeness by touching, kissing and holding hands more often, showing that you enjoy each other's company. Make your spouse feel special.

Sports and physical activities can carry over into the bedroom. Dancing, tennis and hiking are activities that make you feel good about your body. If lack of desire persists at *any* age, see a doctor—it may indicate a medical problem.

• Make time for each other daily. The most important time for most couples is between dinner and bedtime. These moments of relaxation often lend themselves to companionship and intimacy.

Make the most of this time. When interruptions threaten your time together, stop and think about your priorities. Your marriage is an essential part of your life, and it needs to be nourished.

• *Don't let arguments go unresolved.* Sometimes it's easier not to dwell on a disagreement. That's a bad idea when it involves important issues, such as how much money you're spending, disciplining children or even conflicting plans.

RISK: Festering disputes create distance and discomfort—exactly the atmosphere that makes people want to escape a marriage. Set a time to resolve arguments.

BEWARE OF CHEATING...

If you use these techniques and still feel seriously tempted to be unfaithful, don't confess the thought of breaking your vows to your partner. Seek professional help from a therapist, a member of the clergy or another trusted adviser.

He/she will talk to you about the consequences of infidelity and move the thought from a fantasy to the cold, stark light of reality—and tell you about likely outcomes.

TYPICAL CONSEQUENCES: Estrangement from your spouse... spending less time with family...persistent guilt...becoming sneaky...worrying about what your infidelity will do to you and your family.

IF YOU ARE FOUND OUT: Expect your spouse, family, friends and adult children to feel devastating betrayal. Divorce frequently follows.

Also consider talking to a trusted friend, someone who is happily married and who knows both you and your spouse. He/she often can see the joy in your marriage—which you may have lost sight of—and give you perspective. He/she also may be able to prompt you to reconsider what you are contemplating.

IF YOU FALL...

Yielding to temptation doesn't have to ruin a marriage.
If you yielded to temptation once, keep it to yourself. Don't
confess to your spouse. It will be difficult, but you will get past
it. Take the steps mentioned earlier to prevent it from happening
again.

If you enjoyed the escape that the fling provided or cheat
repeatedly, the only hope for your marriage is discussing the
problem jointly with your spouse and a counselor. Doing nothing
almost certainly will wreck the marriage.

About half of marriages survive the humiliation and pain
of infidelity. Those couples that do stay together tend to have
enduring love and goodwill.

■

BEWARE OF INTERNET "AFFAIRS"

Source: **Betsy S. Stone, PhD,** psychologist in private practice, Stamford,
Connecticut.

Internet "affairs" can wreck a marriage—even if the people
communicating over the Internet never actually meet. Internet
relationships often begin in chat rooms or as e-mail on topics
of professional or personal interest.

TRAP: People you have not met face to face can be anything
you want them to be. It's easy for those fantasies projected on
them to seem better than reality—and they can wreak havoc
on a marriage.

DANGER SIGNS: If you start to have romantic feelings about
the person—or begin thinking that the person understands you
better than anyone else.

HELPFUL: Consider counseling to help you understand the
needs the cyber-relationship has been filling.

■

CELEBRATE THE BEGINNING OF
YOUR RELATIONSHIP

Source: **Ellen Kreidman, PhD,** motivational speaker specializing in human relations, El Toro, California, and author of *Is There Sex After Kids?* (St. Martin's).

Celebrate the first time you and your spouse met—not just your wedding anniversary. If you had not met, there would be no wedding anniversary to celebrate. Try re-creating your first meeting on the same day every year—going to the same restaurant or getting together with the same friends at whose party you first met. End your first-meeting anniversary by spending the night in a special hotel.

■

PLAN CREATIVE, ROMANTIC DATES

Source: **Lila Gruzen, PhD, MFCC,** clinical psychologist in private practice, Sherman Oaks, California, and coauthor of *Ten Foolish Dating Mistakes That Men and Women Make (and How to Avoid Them)* (Griffin Publishing Group).

They'll be fun even if you are with someone who turns out to be wrong for you. They need not be expensive. Nor does every date have to involve dinner and a movie or DVD rental.

EXAMPLES: Take a cooking class...go on a nature walk...go ice-skating. Get ideas from friends and the newspaper—or think of what tourists do when they visit your area.

■

MAKE LOVE, NOT WAR—SECRETS OF
MUCH HAPPIER MARRIAGE & MAGIC
FOR TROUBLED RELATIONSHIPS

Source: **Ellen Wachtel, PhD, JD,** psychologist and marital therapist in private practice in New York City. She is author of *We Love Each Other, But...* (St. Martin's).

Couples who are dissatisfied with their marriages don't have to resign themselves to lifelong misery...or get divorced.

Often, simple changes can turn around even the most troubled marriage.

INSIGHT: Recognize that things you have been doing haven't been working.

CHANGE: Stop doing the wrong things...and start doing what creates good feelings.

This sounds simple—and it is. But many couples keep nagging, criticizing, shouting—even while recognizing that those behaviors only make things worse.

It takes only one person to break the vicious cycle of hurt.

STRATEGIES TO IMPROVE ANY MARRIAGE...

REMEMBER THE GOOD TIMES...

To stay motivated through tough times, think back to your courtship. What first attracted you to your spouse?

Now—look to see those qualities in your spouse. The more you pay attention to glimmers of positive feelings, the more positive feelings you will have.

COMPLIMENT GENEROUSLY...

We feel closest to people who make us feel good about ourselves. If you say and do things that build up your partner—and avoid things that make him/her feel worse—your relationship will improve.

Of course, when your marriage is stressed, complimenting your spouse may be the *last* thing you feel like doing. It's much easier to think of all the things he is doing wrong.

REMEMBER: People *don't* change because they're criticized. They change when warmth and goodwill motivate them to please their spouse...or to make their spouses happier.

Train yourself to notice the things you admire about your spouse—no matter how small. Then tell your spouse.

If this still seems difficult, think about how parents behave. They may be frustrated or disappointed with their kids—but they still find ways to acknowledge their good qualities. Adults need this as much as children.

Don't fake admiration. Compliment your spouse on things you admire.

EXAMPLES: *I was really impressed with the way you negotiated our lease...That was a delicious meal—you're a great cook.*

WARM YOUR PARTNER'S HEART...

Early in your relationship, you probably made a point of learning what actions made your partner feel cared for—and you did them. When a marriage is under stress, spouses stop making these loving gestures...and resentment grows.

Look for opportunities to do special things for your partner.

EXAMPLES: Make your spouse a morning cup of tea...offer to watch the kids so your spouse can spend an evening with friends.

PRAISE SMALL CHANGES...

Your partner may take a while to notice that you're acting differently—and even longer to respond with loving gestures of his own.

Be patient. Try to notice any small steps in the right direction. Praising these improvements will encourage your spouse to continue making them.

EXAMPLE: A wife was upset that her husband was always late for dinner. As she made changes to make the relationship more affectionate, he continued to come home late—but started calling to tell her. She thanked him when he called ahead, resisting the urge to add, "I wish you would come home on time." Within a few weeks, he began to arrive at dinnertime.

DON'T PUT OFF SEX...

Many couples avoid sex when they are having marriage problems because they feel emotionally distant. Yet sex can help couples feel closer.

If you're not in the mood, make love anyway. Don't think of it as something you are doing for the marriage...but as something that will make *you* feel good.

POSITIVE ANGER...

All this talk about positive communication doesn't mean that you should bury what bothers you. But express complaints in a constructive way.

• *Raise your complaint when you are not feeling angry about it.* This will help you keep your tone calm—and prevent a nasty fight.

• *Start with something positive.* Your partner is more likely to listen if you acknowledge what he is doing right.

• *Keep it short.* Don't say more than a sentence or two before giving your partner a chance to respond. If you spend a lot of time detailing your point of view, your partner is likely to feel that you are lecturing—and will stop listening.

• *Don't use past hurts to illustrate your gripe.* Your spouse will feel that he can never stop paying for what went wrong in the past. Keep examples current.

• *Avoid your partner's alarm buttons.* Words like "abusive" are overused—and offensive. So are psychological interpretations such as, *You're overreacting because your mother is so controlling.*

• *Listen nondefensively.* Instead of rebutting what your partner says, search for some small part with which you agree.

EXAMPLE: Your partner says, *The minute you walk in the house, you're grumpy. All you do is criticize me.*

INEFFECTIVE RESPONSE: *That's not true. Two days ago, I sat down and had a drink with you. Don't you remember?*

BETTER: I do feel tense when I come home.

Nondefensive listening stops an argument quickly...so you can work on a solution together.

■

BEST WAYS TO SAY "I'M SORRY"

Source: **Jan B. King, president,** The King Group, a human resources and business management company, El Segundo, California. *www.janbking.com.*

A heartfelt note can help you apologize to someone who was once important in your life...

• *Write and rewrite your letter until you could feel good about it in 20 years.*

• *Take full responsibility for your mistakes.* Use the words *I'm sorry* or *I apologize.*

• *Before sending the letter*—spend several days thinking about the letter and how you would feel receiving it.

• *Consider sending it at a meaningful time for the person,* such as a birthday.

• *Give your current address*—but do not expect a response.

• *Do not be upset if you get an angry letter back.* The other person may not have come to terms with what you did.

MYTH: LOVING COUPLES NEVER EVER FIGHT

Source: **James L. Creighton, PhD,** psychologist in Los Gatos, California, who specializes in conflict resolution. He is author of *How Loving Couples Fight* (Aslan Publishing) and coauthor of *Getting Well Again* (Bantam).

It is a myth that happy couples never fight. In fact, they regularly disagree with each other.

What sets loving couples apart is that they disagree in loving ways. They don't let disagreements turn into nasty battles. And their "fights" strengthen, rather than hurt, their relationships.

Handling conflict in a healthy way is a skill that can be learned.

ACCEPT CONFLICT AS NORMAL...

Trying to ignore disagreements or bury resentments doesn't get rid of them. It only allows them to grow below the surface. When we face conflict and deal with it openly, it's easier to let it go and move on. **STEPS TO TAKE...**

• *Express what you feel, not what you think.* Couples who fight lovingly start by talking about how they feel, not about what they think is "wrong" with their partner.

They frame arguments by saying, "I'm hurt/angry/frustrated" rather than, "You're rude/sloppy/a jerk."

When one spouse does something that bothers the other, he/she says so *immediately.* But he describes the specific behavior —not his interpretation.

EXAMPLE: "I was upset when you didn't return my call" expresses how the person feels. "I'm mad because you're inconsiderate" expresses what the person thinks.

It's tempting to blame your negative feelings on the other person's inadequacies. Resist this urge.

Attacking or accusing may make you feel temporarily powerful. But it erodes trust, creating emotional fallout that is very difficult to clean up.

• *Listen—rather than talk—your way out of conflict.* When someone is upset, the natural reaction is to try to talk him out of it. We do this by making excuses for the person...or trying to come up with solutions to the problem...or pointing out all the reasons why there's no need to be upset. But this response implies that the other person doesn't have a right to his feelings. So talking often makes matters worse.

In reality, all it takes to stop the person from being angry is to acknowledge how he feels.

KEY TO EFFECTIVE LISTENING: After your partner has finished speaking, summarize the feelings and ideas that were just expressed. Don't evaluate whether those words are right or wrong ...and don't try to "fix" anything. Just repeat what you've heard.

When you're first learning this technique, it can feel artificial or even patronizing—but it works very effectively.

Many of the couples I work with get around this by using the *five-minute rule.* Either partner can invoke this rule at any time.

HOW IT WORKS: One person has five minutes to speak without interruption. Then the other person has five minutes. If you can't decide who should start, flip a coin. Sometimes you both may need *another* turn to speak.

By the end of the second round, both people have usually gotten most of their frustration out of the way and can start discussing the problem more constructively.

FIGHT FAIRLY...

Happy couples follow several unspoken rules that keep their small arguments from escalating into big ones...

• *Stick to the issue.* If he's mad because she's not ready to leave at the agreed-upon time, that's the subject the loving couple talks about.

They don't get sidetracked by accusations, such as, "You don't care how I feel" or, "One of us has to live in the real world."

They also don't keep bringing up past grievances. If an issue keeps coming up over and over, they'll talk about it—but not as a way of punishing each other when they're arguing about something else.

• *Don't hit below the belt.* Loving couples don't try to hurt each other by attacking sensitive areas, such as weight, job status, in-laws, etc.

• *Don't drag other people into it.* Don't say things such as, "I'm not the only person who feels this way. Your sister and brother do, too."

Trying to bolster your side of the argument by bringing up someone else not only escalates the fight but also poisons your partner's relationship with that person.

Some couples find it helpful to make these rules explicit—and remind each other gently if one of them breaks a rule.

Don't turn these reminders into occasions to gloat. A simple reminder, such as, "Remember, we agreed not to do that" usually is enough.

IMPORTANT: The best time to agree on rules is right *after* a fight, when you've cooled down enough to talk reasonably. The memory of the fight you just had—and how unpleasant it was not to be following the rules—will motivate you to do things differently.

HUDDLE TO SOLVE PROBLEMS...

Sometimes just hearing each other out helps partners understand one another's point of view—and resolves the conflict. When that's not enough, happy couples work together to find a better way of dealing with the issue. **PROBLEM-SOLVING STEPS...**

• *Agree on what the problem is.*
• *Brainstorm alternative solutions.*
• *Agree on a solution that best meets your needs and those of your partner.*
• *Agree on a way to put the solution into practice.*
• *Evaluate how well the solution is working.*

■

MARRIAGES *DO* SURVIVE AFFAIRS

Source: **K. Daniel O'Leary, PhD,** professor of psychology, State University of New York at Stony Brook, whose research survey was published in *Journal of Sex & Marital Therapy.*

Couples therapy is almost always useful. The therapist helps the couple analyze how the affair happened—making sure neither partner bears all the blame. Couples learn that regaining trust will take a great deal of time, so they do not expect rapid resumption of intimacy. The person who had the affair learns how to handle his/her partner's outbursts of anger and periods of depression.

GOOD NEWS: Most couples who receive help after an affair stay together.

■

HOW TO KEEP YOUR MARRIAGE HAPPY AND STOP TROUBLES BEFORE THEY START

Source: **John Gottman, PhD,** professor of psychology at University of Washington in Seattle and codirector of the Seattle Marital and Family Institute, Box 15644, Seattle 98115. He is author of *Why Marriages Succeed or Fail...and How You Can Make Yours Last* (Fireside).

Traditional marriage counseling focuses on repairing long-standing problems. Most troubled couples wait an average of six years before they seek help.

A new approach is to teach relationship skills early, before negative habits become entrenched and destructive.

At the Seattle Marital and Family Institute, we have studied hundreds of couples to see what leads some to happiness and others to break up. Based on our research, we have developed techniques to strengthen marriages and help spouses deal with conflict.

MARRIAGE EDUCATION...

• *Balanced marital ecology.* Critical to any marriage is a healthy relationship between positive and negative emotions toward each other. In case after case, we have found that the ideal ratio is five times as many positive feelings as negative ones.

This ratio of positive to negative feelings not only nurtures your relationship but also builds up your emotional reserves when arguments and ill feelings strike—as they do in any close relationship.

IMPORTANT: Don't expect to eliminate *all* negative emotions toward your spouse. Couples need to air and resolve disagreements.

Most stable couples see their conflicts not as divisive but as shared and strengthening experiences.

Some negativity may also help keep sexual passion alive as couples first withdraw and then renew their affection.

• *Accentuate the positive.* To keep your own positive ratio high, don't allow everyday tasks and commitments to crowd out thoughtfulness, affection and closeness. Give thoughtful compliments...call each other during the day just to check in ...and share private time together.

Consciously appreciating your spouse's good qualities also helps you maintain the vital positive–negative ratio when negativity appears. **HELPFUL...**

• List your partner's positive contributions to your life together. Reflect on how much harder life would be without those contributions.

When you find yourself mentally criticizing your mate, "interrupt" your thinking with positive items from the list.

• Dispel negative feelings after a disagreement by looking through vacation picture albums or remembering your best times together...even reading old love letters.

• See the relationship as half-full rather than as half-empty to defuse potentially irritating situations.

EXAMPLE: If your partner leaves dirty dishes in the sink for several nights in a row, don't blow up. Think of all the other things he/she does to help the house run smoothly.

• *Complain without being critical.* Voicing grievances is healthy and positive in a marriage. Attacking your spouse's character is not.

IMPORTANT: Criticism often begins with the word *you,* as in, "You're too irresponsible to call when you're going to be late."

Blaming and accusing leads to anger and resentment.

BETTER: Complaints that begin with the word *I* and deal strictly with the specific behavior you would like changed. Addressing an issue rather than a character flaw allows room for discussion.

EXAMPLE: "I wish you had let me know you wouldn't be home on time."

Contempt, which goes beyond criticism to insults, name-calling, hostile humor and mockery, must be *completely banned* from marital discussions.

You can guard against the temptation to voice contempt by not seeing arguments as a way to retaliate or exhibit moral superiority.

Instead of criticism, contempt and *kitchen-sinking*—dragging a multitude of grievances into an argument—I advocate *gentle confrontation*.

This involves emphasizing that you love your spouse and that your complaint concerns behavior he can, indeed, change. You can also say that you are bringing up the issue only to strengthen your relationship.

• *Structure your arguments.* When arguments intensify, both spouses may experience *emotional flooding*—sharply elevated heart rate and blood pressure...and increased adrenaline secretion.

All stimulate a *fight-or-flight reaction*—an attack or a defensive withdrawal. That is always fatal to mutual understanding or problem solving.

HELPFUL: Put a 15-minute limit on arguments. If either of you feels flooded, call a 20-minute time-out.

Since continued negative thoughts and feelings of revenge will only reinforce flooding, we stress self-soothing during the time-out.

EXAMPLE: Say to yourself, "We have a good marriage" or, "We still love each other."

When both of you are calm, continue the discussion for another 15 minutes.

• *Communicate nondefensively.* When you react defensively, you unintentionally sidetrack arguments rather than resolve them. In addition, the stonewalling defense of silence and withdrawal usually leads the blocked spouse to attack harder in hopes of getting through.

Instead, use two strategies...*non-defensive speech,* and—what we call—*validating.*

• Nondefensive speech cools down the argument and helps both parties feel more positive. Even if you can't give sincere praise and admiration, really listening signals that you understand your partner's feelings, even if you don't share them. *Example:* "That's a good point."

• Validating—or verbally empathizing with your spouse's emotions and viewpoint—encourages discussion, openness and sharing. The nonvalidating statement, "You always ignore me when you come home from work," separates you further. The validating approach, "I understand you're tired after work but I would still like to feel you're happy to see me," helps bring you together.

■

BEFORE GETTING MARRIED: PLAN YOUR LIFE TOGETHER

Source: **Everett De Morier,** motivational speaker on marriage, business and success, Vestal, New York. He is author of *Crib Notes for the First Year of Marriage: A Survival Guide for Newlyweds* (Fairview Press).

D o not assume your two previously separate lives will somehow merge and work well. Set mutual goals...find activities you both enjoy. Brainstorm by naming things you always wanted to do but did not want to try alone—and places you have always wanted to go. Think of where you see *yourself* in five years—and 20 years. Then think about where you see yourselves *as a couple* in five and 20 years.

■

SECRETS OF LASTING LOVE—IT'S WONDERFUL...DELIGHTFUL! DELOVELY!

Source: **Ayala Malach Pines, PhD,** professor of psychology at Ben-Gurion University School of Business, Beer-Sheva, Israel. She is author of *Falling in Love: Why We Choose the Lovers We Choose* (Routledge).

T hey say that falling in love is wonderful—and it's true. In those magic days when you first find someone special, skies look brighter, birds sing more sweetly and everything seems possible. There's simply something mysterious about the experience.

But falling in love has down-to-earth lessons to teach as well...and they can be immensely valuable at every stage of a relationship.

If you want love, you've got to know where to look. Understanding your own *love code* can guide you to the choice of the right partner. For those already in a relationship, regularly recalling how it all began provides a bedrock of strength—and healing—throughout a long marriage.

WHY DO WE FALL IN LOVE?...

Who ever loved that loved not at first sight? asked Shakespeare.

The answer seems to be most people. Only one in 10 lasting relationships begins with an electric moment of mutual attraction. Usually, feelings of interest and attraction take time to catch fire.

Modern psychology has identified some elements that fuel the flame...

• *Emotional arousal* puts men and women in the mood for love. Under the spell of pleasurable excitement or even shared catastrophes, you're likely to interpret pounding of the pulse and quickening of the breath as signs of love toward an attractive person.

LOVE LESSON: Put stimulating situations to work for you. Meet prospective mates through hiking clubs, gyms, etc. The best dates are at rousing concerts and plays—not at posh restaurants.

• *Proximity.* When we see the same person over and over, our feelings (positive or negative) are likely to intensify. Presence—not absence—makes the heart grow fonder. That helps explain romance with the girl/boy next door or in the next office.

LOVE LESSON: Focus on activities where, if you meet an attractive person, you will see him/her repeatedly—classes, church groups, etc. Bars are a bad bet, unless they are full of regulars and "everybody knows your name."

• *Similarity.* As every matchmaker knows, people with lots in common—background, values, intelligence, education—are most likely to fall in love.

While opposites attract, the odds of a lasting, satisfying relationship are far better when you start out on the same page.

LOVE LESSON: Cultivate friendships with people with whom you share a great deal.

• *Being yourself.* Most men respond first to physical appearance ...and then only with time discover a woman's inner beauty.

Women often recall that a man's attentive, caring or sympathetic personality initially piqued their interest. So it makes sense to play socially accepted roles—put your best foot forward simply to get past the first barriers to acquaintance.

But since falling in love is a multi-stage process, drop the mask as quickly as you can—and reveal your true self. Lasting relationships are built on solid ground.

IMPORTANT: You should make no secret of your attraction to —and appreciation of—the person you care about.

VERY PERSONAL CHEMISTRY...

We fall in love with people who satisfy our needs. What qualities are most important to you?

- *Attentive listening?*
- *A warm, supportive personality?*
- *Respect for your space and solitude requirements?*

The odds of love are best with someone who offers those qualities. You'll *awaken* love by being sensitive to his needs and striving to satisfy them.

One side of love defies rational analysis. Why do we fall hard for people we don't see regularly...with whom we share few interests ...who aren't particularly attractive, caring or attentive?

Many psychologists believe the answer lies in the unconscious. Early in life, we construct a mental picture from those most important to us—parents, of course, but maybe siblings and others as well. When we meet a person who fits the image, sparks fly, even if he wouldn't have much appeal to others.

Understanding the source of your unique romantic image is vital if you repeatedly fall in love with the wrong people. Choosing partners who make you unhappy is often a pattern with roots in needs that were aroused, but never met, in the distant past.

TO UNDERSTAND YOUR ROMANTIC CODE: Think about the two or three people who kindled your greatest passion...

- *What did they have in common?*
- *Does anything about them make you think of problems with your parents?*

Realize that the devil-may-care type who turns you on can lead to nothing but disappointment. This can make it easier to accept the enduring warmth of a real—if less exciting—relationship.

MAKING LOVE LAST...

In many marriages, the magic of love is a distant memory, replaced by boredom and hostility. Day-to-day quarrels over money, in-laws, household tasks, etc. make it easy to miss the core of the conflict—often the very same thing that first attracted the two people to each other.

EXAMPLES: A woman complains that her husband is *not assertive.* But when they first met, she was charmed by his easy-going nature. A man says his wife *explodes at the slightest provocation.* Way back when, he was taken by her energy and the fact that things always happened around her.

Recalling why you fell in love can be a first step to restoring harmony in a marriage. Remember—we often choose a partner because he awakens unresolved childhood problems, which remain magnetic and infuriating. **EXAMPLES...**

• *The daughter of a cold father* is drawn to the calm reserve of her future husband...but eventually angered by that reserve.

• *A man whose mother was obsessively close* is at first deeply attracted to the warmth and attentiveness of his wife...but eventually feels smothered.

If each partner can understand the other—and then take at least small steps toward giving what each desperately wants (more connection for the wife, more space for the husband)—the result can be renewed love, deep personal growth and healing ...the full fruit of love's blossom.

■

QUESTIONS THAT KEEP LOVE ALIVE

Source: **Jonathan Robinson,** psychotherapist and seminar leader, Santa Barbara, California. He is author of *Instant Insight: 200 Ways to Create the Life You Really Want* (Health Communications).

Communication in a relationship is vital to its survival. **HERE ARE QUESTIONS FOR EACH PARTNER IN THE RELATIONSHIP...**

ASK YOUR PARTNER: What helps you feel most loved by me?... Do you know what you do that makes me feel most loved?

ASK YOURSELF: What act of love or kindness can I do for my partner this week?...What problems are we having that we are not talking about?...How can we talk about them?

HELPFUL: Plan to spend quality time together at least twice a week. Think about what you really love about your partner... and what fun things you can do together. Then work together to plan them.

■

KEYS TO BETTER RELATIONSHIPS

Source: **Bill Marriott's** advice on human relations, quoted in *Finish Strong* by Richard Capen, Jr., former media executive and US government official (Harper-SanFrancisco).

Be humble, says Bill Marriott, chairman of the Marriott Corporation. **HIS ADVICE...**

THE SIX MOST IMPORTANT WORDS: *I admit that I was wrong.*
THE FIVE MOST IMPORTANT: *You did a great job.*
THE FOUR MOST IMPORTANT: *What do you think?*
THE THREE MOST IMPORTANT: *Could you please?*
THE TWO MOST IMPORTANT: *Thank you.*
THE MOST IMPORTANT: *We.*
THE LEAST IMPORTANT: *I.*

■

PHYSICAL ATTRACTION

Source: **Barbara De Angelis, PhD,** specialist in human relations and personal growth, Los Angeles. She is author of *Real Moments for Lovers* (Delacorte Press).

Look for beauty in your partner—beauty that attracted you physically in the first place. Just as someone's eyes can make you tingle with pleasure or feel filled with strength, courage or hatred, so your eyes can make your partner feel your love. Look at small things you admire—the way he/she moves his hands, the curve of his back, the texture of his hair. Use your eyes to search for reasons to fall more deeply in love. ■

NEVER GO TO BED MAD AND OTHER MARRIAGE MYTHS

Source: **Pepper Schwartz, PhD,** professor of sociology at University of Washington, Seattle, and senior fellow of Council on Contemporary Families. She is author of several books, including *Everything You Know About Love and Sex Is Wrong: Twenty-Five Relationship Myths Redefined to Achieve Happiness and Fulfillment in Your Intimate Life* (Perigee).

Many marriages fail because people base their attitudes and behavior on widely held beliefs that simply aren't true. One of the most destructive is the belief that if you desire someone else, something must be wrong with your relationship.

EXAMPLE: You fantasize about a coworker, then worry that you're "betraying" your spouse. Or you see your spouse eyeing someone and question his/her fidelity.

Human beings have their heads turned by others. It's just the way it is. It's not a sign of infidelity.

Of course, there is a big difference between desire and action. Fantasy is harmless and can be better than reality.

Other myths to watch out for...

MYTH: *Your spouse should be your best friend.*

Women in particular often want their husbands to be their best friends. They want them to reveal everything...share their deepest feelings...chat for hours about relationships. Men are rarely like that—so their wives are disappointed.

REALITY: You look for different characteristics in a spouse than you do in a friend. A best friend might think the same way you do and enjoy the same things. But when you evaluate a potential spouse, odds are that you consider sexual attraction ...parenting potential...financial solvency, etc.

You can have a great marriage and *not* be best friends. Couples can have fun and enjoy their time together without seeing the world in exactly the same way.

MYTH: *You should never go to bed mad.*

Simmering anger invariably comes to a boil...and every couple is happier when they "let off steam." Right? Wrong.

Nothing gets solved when people are enraged. In fact, expressing anger produces even more anger from the surge of adrenaline and other stress hormones.

It's better to go to bed mad than to say or do something you'll regret later...

- *Tell your spouse, "I can't handle this right now."*
- *Agree on a time to work out your disagreements.*
- *Once you're calm, slip praise and compliments into the discussion.*

EXAMPLE: If you are upset about a purchase your partner made, remember to mention that, most of the time, you agree with and respect his money management.

One researcher found that it takes five positive comments to undo the anger-causing impact of one negative remark.

MYTH: *You should always be 100% honest.*

People get angry when I say that it is not always good to be honest with your partner and share the intimate details of your life. Should a man tell his wife he kissed a neighbor three years ago? Should a woman tell her husband that she has a harmless crush on a coworker?

Don't use your partner as your confessional. Think twice before you tell something that will forever cause your partner to doubt your word or be jealous of your relationships with friends.

MYTH: *Sex that is unsatisfying in the beginning can always be fixed.*

Great sex won't necessarily keep a couple together. But bad sex leads to frustration, alienation and/or anger. If sex is unsatisfactory early on, don't assume things will get better. Some problems —impotence, painful intercourse and premature ejaculation— may be solved. **OTHERS ARE UNLIKELY TO CHANGE...**

- *Differences in desire.* If one partner rarely wants sex and the other wants it a lot, the relationship will suffer.
- *Incompatible sexual tastes.* If one partner has "kinky" desires and the other doesn't, tension is inevitable.

Most partners can learn to satisfy each other, but only if their sexual desires are similar.

MYTH: *No marriage can survive infidelity.*

Few experiences are more painful than discovering your partner has been unfaithful. But an affair is not necessarily a sign that your marriage is over.

There are many reasons why a spouse may see someone else—the need to feel attractive to others...loneliness when a partner is away...giving in to an opportunity, etc. But these say little about the quality of a marriage or the strength of the unfaithful spouse's commitment.

If you have been betrayed, ask yourself what is most important to you. If it's sexual loyalty, then an affair *can* mean the end of the marriage. But if what you value is your partner and the other good things in your marriage, it's worth making the effort to work through the crisis.

If you are the offender, knowing there is a chance for forgiveness might mean the difference between choosing to stay or leave. Often, the discovery of an affair provides the impetus to seek counseling to strengthen a marriage.

■

BETTER COMMUNICATION FOR COUPLES

Source: **Harville Hendrix, PhD,** cofounder and president of The Institute for Imago Relationship Therapy, Winter Park, Florida. He is author of *Getting the Love You Want* (Owl Books) and *Keeping the Love You Find* (Pocket Books).

Effective communication is essential to resolving conflicts between partners.

But too often, discussions become mired in an attack-defense-counterattack exchange that leaves each person feeling unheard and negated.

To end this destructive pattern, I worked with Helen Hunt—my wife and Imago Institute cofounder—to develop a system we call *Intentional Dialogue.*

This method may take practice—but give it a chance. When it is employed properly, communication will become clearer... your connection will grow deeper...and issues will simply dissolve over time.

Use Intentional Dialogue *whenever* careful listening and complete understanding count...or to discuss something that has upset you...or when you are addressing a topic that might be touchy.

To begin, one partner makes a statement. **THEN THE OTHER FOLLOWS THESE THREE STEPS...**

MIRROR YOUR PARTNER...

Repeat the message in your own words. This indicates your willingness to understand your partner's perspective and ensures that you have accurately understood what has been said.

Taking time to mirror also halts a defensive response to what you *thought* you heard.

Continue this step until you agree that the meaning has gotten across.

EXAMPLE: *If I heard you correctly, you feel that if I don't look at you when you are talking to me, I am not interested in what you are saying.*

VALIDATE THE VIEWPOINT...

Affirming your partner's viewpoint does not necessarily mean you agree. Rather, it acknowledges that his/her position is a legitimate way of regarding the situation.

Preface a validation with phrases such as *What you say makes sense to me because...* or *I can understand that....*

EXAMPLE: *I can understand that when I don't look at you, I appear uninterested.*

EXPRESS EMPATHY...

Although you may not share the emotions, you can recognize and appreciate them on some level. Lead-ins such as *I can imagine that you feel...* or *When you experience that, you feel...* can be the start of empathetic communication.

EXAMPLE: *I can imagine that when I appear uninterested, you would feel rejected and angry.*

RESOLUTION...

Once the sender confirms the communication has been understood and accepted, reverse the receiver-sender roles and begin the process again.

Continue until you both feel the current discussion has been concluded.

■

MAKING UP NOT SO HARD TO DO

Source: **Bonnie Eaker Weil, PhD,** New York City–based psychologist specializing in relationships. *http://doctorbonnie.com.* She is author of *Make Up, Don't Break Up* (Adams Media) and *Adultery, The Forgivable Sin* (Hastings House).

My patients are always relieved when I tell them that fighting with a partner is not a bad thing. It can make a relationship even *more* passionate.

I worry most about relationships in which the partners are too polite to argue—adultery is most common here.

To restore intimacy following an argument, you must go *counterintuitive.* This means getting close when you feel yourselves pulled apart. You must consciously shift gears *away* from conflict and back to romance.

• *Reconnect physically*—kiss, touch, gaze into each other's eyes. Snuggling is magical. It reverses the flow of negative hormones caused by fighting and releases "cuddle" hormones that promote good feeling.

Being physical is particularly important for men, who experience actual physical discomfort when in conflict with loved ones. They get headaches...their hands sweat...they may feel nauseated. Acts of physical affection, such as holding and hugging, help men regain their equilibrium and feel "safe" with their feelings.

• *Try humor and fun.* This helps redirect your energy toward —rather than away from—each other.

EXAMPLE: After an argument, my husband dances me in circles around the room to remind us of the fun we have together. We invariably end up laughing and are able to refocus on the importance of our relationship—rather than whatever we were fighting about.

• *Give up the idea of winning the fight.* If both of you win, you're winners. If one of you wins and the other loses, you're both losers.

Fights aren't about being right. They are about feelings. Try to understand your partner's point of view and honor his/her feelings.

■

CAN YOUR MARRIAGE LAST?
TAKE DR. GOULSTON'S LOVE QUIZ

Source: **Mark Goulston, MD,** assistant clinical professor, UCLA Neuro-psychiatric Institute, Los Angeles. He is author of *The 6 Secrets of a Lasting Relationship: How to Fall in Love Again—and Stay There* (Putnam). He is cofounder of the Web site *www.couplescompany.com.*

In my 33 years as a psychiatrist, I have found that the elements of a lasting relationship are hidden in plain sight. The "secret" elements are chemistry...respect...enjoyment... acceptance...trust...empathy.

When these elements are abundant, a relationship is vital and strong. When any one of them is in short supply, the relationship is troubled.

To make a relationship last...

• *Identify where it has deteriorated.* Have dialogue to air resentments, correct misunderstandings and develop solutions to which both partners commit.

• *Take steps to keep the six elements out in the open,* where they can be nurtured by you and your partner—so you can stay in love.

KEEP THE CHEMISTRY...

Chemistry is the passion that sweeps you away when you first fall in love.

TEST YOURSELF: How often are you turned on by the way your partner looks dressed and undressed?

ANSWERS: 1/Rarely...2/Sometimes...3/Often.

EARN EACH OTHER'S RESPECT...

This has more to do with how good a person you are—and how good a person your partner is—than how good each of you makes the other feel. You demonstrate respect by how well you listen.

TEST YOURSELF: How often do you listen to your partner and hear him/her all the way through without interrupting?
ANSWERS: 1/Rarely...2/Sometimes...3/Often.

ENJOY EACH OTHER...

This is about having fun being together. When you're with your spouse—or think about him—it makes you feel lighter and puts a smile on your face. Unpleasant people—judgmental, easy to disappoint and difficult to please—drain your energy.
TEST YOURSELF: How often do you and your partner dine alone together?
ANSWERS: 1/Rarely...2/Sometimes...3/Often.

ACCEPT YOUR PARTNER AS IS...

It is better to hope for change, rather than to keep acceptance contingent on changes being made. When acceptance is missing, partners feel judged and as if they can't do anything right.
TEST YOURSELF: How often do you feel you can be yourself with your partner?
ANSWERS: 1/Rarely...2/Sometimes...3/Often.

BUILD TRUST...

Trust makes it safe to confide fears and dreams without concern that what you say will be exploited, betrayed, trivialized or ridiculed. It takes seconds to destroy trust—and years to rebuild it.
TEST YOURSELF: How often are you able to tell your partner things you feel embarrassed or ashamed about?
ANSWERS: 1/Rarely...2/Sometimes...3/Often.

EMPATHY TO DEFUSE RESENTMENT...

Empathy is about understanding and feeling understood by your partner. It's asking, "What's it like for my partner right now?" Don't presume you know.
TEST YOURSELF: How frequently do you feel understood by your partner?
ANSWERS: 1/Rarely...2/Sometimes...3/Often.

HOW DO YOU RATE?...

If you and your partner scored 3s across the board, you have the basis for a lasting relationship. Congratulations!

If, however, either you or your partner scored less than 3 in any of the six areas, you may want to improve.

Set aside time to talk through when and why any of those areas deteriorated. Make every effort to have a dialogue instead of a debate...to talk *with* instead of *at* or *over*...to listen openly rather than defensively.

Then decide what each of you specifically needs to do now to restore the chemistry, respect, enjoyment, acceptance, trust and empathy so that you can fall in love again—and stay there.

■

KEEPING LOVE ALIVE...CREATIVE IDEAS

Source: **Michael Webb,** syndicated columnist in Cary, North Carolina, and author of *The RoMANtic's Guide: Hundreds of Creative Tips for a Lifetime of Love* (Hyperion). *www.theromantic.com.*

R omance shouldn't be reserved for special occasions, holidays or just to get out of the doghouse.

Romance has little to do with jewelry, chocolates, roses and expensive dinners. It is a combination of all the little—and big—things you do to tell your partner "I love you." **SUGGESTIONS FOR KEEPING ROMANCE ALIVE YEAR-ROUND...**

• *Kiss a Spot-of-the-Week.* Each weekend, I designate a place on my wife's body to kiss. It might be her right eyebrow, left ear or elsewhere. I kiss that place repeatedly the following week.

• *Keep dating each other—even if you're married.* This advice rarely gets followed. Plan at least one date each week. Be creative —they don't all have to be dinner dates. My wife and I have been on dates to museums, to the zoo, on a train and even to bookstores. We've also enjoyed the Quarter Date, in which we spend $10 in quarters on arcade games (only two-player games), kiddie rides, tourist binoculars, gumball machines.

• *Celebrate your monthly anniversary.* Don't wait a whole year to do something special. For our 75th (monthly) wedding anniversary, I created a coloring book for my wife. Using a black marker, I doodled pictures of our memorable experiences and had them bound. Periodically we take out the book—and a pack of crayons—and relive the memories.

- *Surprise your sweetie...*
  - Tie a nonbreakable gift to a three-foot string. Attach it, with some streamers and balloons, to the handle of an automatic garage door. When your honey comes home, the gift will rise to greet him/her.
  - Hide confetti or flower petals atop a ceiling fan.
  - Pack lunch for your spouse. Spice it up by carving a heart on an apple or a pear...include love notes, a favorite comic strip or Hershey kisses.
  - Buy glow-in-the-dark stars from a toy store, and arrange a loving message on the ceiling above your bed before leaving on a business trip.

■

REMARRIAGE—HOW TO DO IT RIGHT

Source: **Diane Sollee, MSW,** marital therapist and director of Smart Marriages and the Coalition for Marriage, Family and Couples Education, 5310 Belt Rd. NW, Washington, DC 20015. *www.smartmarriages.com.*

With or without children, the majority of those who divorce remarry...and 65% of those *second* marriages end in divorce.

One of the biggest reasons for marriage failure is our belief in the myth of the *perfect person.*

When a spouse falls short of our ideal, we blame him/her for what's wrong in the marriage.

REALITY: Marriage is not about perfection. How you behave in a relationship will either keep your love alive...or kill it.

CAUSES OF MARITAL FAILURE...

- *Thinking you've found the right one.* People who remarry tend to be even more deluded about finding the perfect person than they were the first time around.

  BETTER: Don't over-romanticize your partner's attributes— acknowledge his flaws.

- *Blaming your former spouse for the failure of your first marriage.* Most marriages fail because the partners lacked the proper tools to address problems.

BETTER: Take communication and conflict-management cours-es with your new partner to learn coping skills when conflicts arise.

My Web site, *www.smartmarriages.com,* is a clearinghouse to help couples locate such courses in their areas. Most cours-es last one to two days.

• *Believing you are in a loveless marriage...and walking away from it.* Many people leave marriages based on the mistaken belief that couples in love don't argue.

Love doesn't mean you'll always agree. All couples disagree —and about the same basic things. **COUPLES WHO SUCCESSFULLY MANAGE THEIR DISAGREEMENTS...**

• *Don't try to make their partners exactly like them.* They talk through the disagreements and listen to each other's opinions with respect.

• *Accept irreconcilable differences.* Every couple has approximate-ly 10...so understand what they are and fence them off. Don't let differences contaminate the love you feel for each other.

Discuss problems without assigning blame. Surround all requests with expressions of love.

• *Expecting everyone in the newly blended family to care about each other immediately.* With stepfamilies, the main rule is to be flexible and realistic. Children don't care about someone just because he/she is married to their parent. It takes an av-erage of four years to build trust and establish new rituals.

■

WHAT IS YOUR SLEEPING POSITION?

Source: **Mark Goulston, MD,** psychiatrist in private practice in Santa Monica, California, and author of *The 6 Secrets of a Lasting Relationship: How to Fall in Love Again—and Stay There* (Putnam). He is cofounder of the Web site *www. couplescompany.com.*

Your sleeping position with your partner says a lot about your relationship. It reflects feelings of closeness, safety, trust, dis-tance or indifference. **EXAMPLES...**

• *Spooning,* when one partner snuggles behind the other, shows positive emotional interdependence, especially if you sometimes reverse positions.

- *Leg hug,* with partners touching legs, acknowledges the relationship but shows a fair amount of independence.
- *Cliffhanger,* when people lie in near-fetal positions at opposite sides of the bed, can indicate relationship trouble. Positions change and do not always mean the same thing. If you have usually slept in a close, loving position and now feel more comfortable sleeping farther apart, consider whether your relationship is under stress.

■

WHAT YOUR DISAGREEMENT SAYS ABOUT YOUR RELATIONSHIP

Source: **Seth Eisenberg, CEO,** Practical Application of Intimate Relationship Skills, 318 Indian Trace, PMB158, Weston, Florida 33326. *www.pairs.com.*

First three minutes of newlyweds' marital disagreements indicate the likelihood of divorce. Couples who quickly escalate disputes are much *less* likely to stay married.

SELF-DEFENSE: Avoid relationship-damaging behaviors, particularly contempt, defensiveness, criticism and belligerence.

■

SECRETS OF GETTING ALONG WITH YOUR EX FOR THE SAKE OF THE CHILDREN AND EVERYONE'S SANITY

Source: **Nailah Shami,** author of *Taking the High Road: How to Cope with Your Ex-Husband, Maintain Your Sanity and Raise Your Child in Peace* (Plume). Ms. Shami is a divorced mother of one child and a registered counselor specializing in personal growth and wellness in Redmond, Washington.

Marriages end all the time. But when a divorce involves children, the adults have a lifelong connection to each other. To ensure a healthful, positive environment for your children, you must create a way to get along with your ex-spouse, make sound decisions and communicate effectively—no matter how difficult.

• *Only discuss issues related to your children.* Be willing to duck any nastiness your ex throws your way, and just stick to what must be resolved about your children. Speak calmly and evenly in all situations.

• *Be specific.* If it is a sensitive issue, such as overdue child support, make your request specific, such as, *Can I come by and pick up the check...or will you drop it off today?*

• *Suppress negative feelings toward your ex.* This is a continuous process. Positive affirmations work well for me when my ex-husband is being nasty or difficult. Use this inner chatter to change your behavior.

EXAMPLES: I'm feeling perfectly calm...I'm willing to communicate pleasantly...I'm doing what is in the best interests of my children.

If your ex-spouse is extremely difficult, try playacting. Think of a favorite actor and what he/she would do in your situation. Then put on a show. I plant a Julia Roberts smile on my face during especially trying times.

If you are really upset, wait until the conversation has ended and write out the nastiness. It's amazing what relief you get from this type of release.

REMEMBER: Difficult conversations only *seem* to last for an eternity.

• *Demonstrate how your ex-spouse's negative behavior affects your children.* Point out the benefits of positive behavior. If you can't find a benefit, provide a negative consequence—*If you continue to be late meeting John after school, I'm going to set up after-school soccer for him. He deserves to be shown that he is loved and cared for.*

• *Never put children in the middle.* Negotiations should take place when the children are out of the house—or at least out of hearing range. Children deserve to have parents who can communicate effectively...and who will make sure their lives flow smoothly.

• *Reward yourself.* In order to extend this level of grace and pleasantry, you need to nurture yourself—so you feel loved and cared for. Build in rewards for your positive behavior—dinner out with friends, a movie, etc.

■